Pet Health Journal

A 6 Month Journal For
Medications, Exams, & Healthy Living

Internal Medicine For Pet Parents Series

Yvonne Brandenburg, RVT, VTS (SAIM)
Ashley DiPrete, RVT, VTS (SAIM)

Dedication

To all the families and pets we've had the honor of working with over the years.

Table of Contents

How to Use This Journal

You've got in your hands a tool to fight the chronic disease your pet was diagnosed with. Whether your dog or cat was diagnosed with kidney disease, liver disease, or any of the other diseases they can get, our goal is for this journal to help you keep track of your pet's health.

Here's a breakdown of the sections:
1. The first section is "Basic Pet Info" where you can include a photo, your contact information, insurance policy information, and basic veterinary information.
2. The "Veterinary Exams & Treatment Plans" section is the perfect place to keep track of the next veterinary appointment, and your vets' recommendations or medication changes.
3. In the "Medications" section keep track of medication information including which pharmacy you get the medications from along with their contact info.
4. Next is "Quality of Life" that includes a quality of life scale table to calculate your pets' daily/weekly quality of life (QOL) number if needed. This number can be tracked in the treatment journal section.
5. The "Treatment Journal" is the main part of this journal. You'll find six monthly sections to record all the essentials including how your pet is doing on a daily basis.
6. Each month includes a monthly calendar to track quality of life numbers and appointments. There is also a place to add comments about the month.
7. For each month there are five individual weeks to keep track of your pets' daily life.
   a. Included is a medication schedule to keep track of up to ten medications daily and up to four times a day that can be customized to your pets' individual needs.
   b. There is a daily and weekly quality of life number spot to help track how your pet is doing over time.
   c. Of course, there is also a spot to write comments for the week.

We hope this journal helps you keep your furry family member happy and healthy!

Basic Pet Info

My Pet's Info

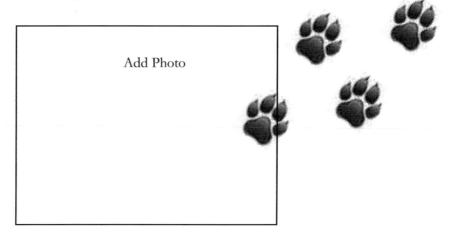

Add Photo

Name:	
Date of Birth:	
Owners Name:	
Contact Info:	Home #: Cell #: Other #: Email:
Pet Insurance Info	Name: Website: Phone #: Policy #: Email:
Microchip # or Markings	
Comments	

Medical Information

Medical Conditions	
Blood Type:	
Allergies:	
Vaccine History	
Animal Poison Control	Website: **ASPCA** https://www.aspca.org/pet-care/animal-poison-control Phone #: USA: **1-888-426-4435** Other: Comments:
Primary Care Veterinarian	**Name:** Address: Phone #: Email:
Specialty Care Veterinarian	**Name:** Address: Phone #: Email:
Other Veterinarian	**Name:** Address: Phone #: Email:
Comments	

Veterinary Exams & Treatment Plans

Appointments

Date & Time	Veterinarian	Weight	Diagnostics or Treatments	Plan, Medication Changes, Comments	Exam Due Date
			Yearly Exam Yearly blood screen		

Date & Time	Veterinarian	Weight	Diagnostics or Treatments	Plan, Medication Changes, Comments	Exam Due Date

Date & Time	Veterinarian	Weight	Diagnostics or Treatments	Plan, Medication Changes, Comments	Exam Due Date

Date & Time	Veterinarian	Weight	Diagnostics or Treatments	Plan, Medication Changes, Comments	Exam Due Date

Medications

Medication List

Date	Name	Strength	Instructions	Refills/Pharmacy	Comment

Date	Name	Strength	Instructions	Refills/Pharmacy	Comment

Pharmacy Types

There are many options for purchasing prescription medications. Typically, the veterinary practice will carry most common medications prescribed for your pet. In the case they do not carry a specific medication, your veterinarian may recommend a traditional pharmacy or a compounding pharmacy. Medications that are also used in human medicine may be easily dispensed from any pharmacy such as the ones found in your local grocery store or neighborhood pharmacy.

However, there are veterinary specific medications and most human pharmacies will not carry them. That is where online pharmacies typically come in.

Another issue may be that the dose for your particular pet falls between what is normally available, or maybe you are having trouble getting the medication into your pet, for these situations a compounding pharmacy may be the right answer for you. A compounding pharmacy takes the drug and makes it into the perfect strength or perfect formulation. These can be in the form of tablets, capsules, liquids, or even topical options. Liquids are usually a great option for small dogs and for cats.

It is important that no matter which type of pharmacy you use for getting your medications that they are licensed and reputable. Unfortunately, like with any business, there are places that either sell knock off medications or they do not follow the strict guidelines set forth by the government regulators like the FDA or DEA. If you are concerned you can always ask a member of your veterinary team if the pharmacy you would like to use is reputable.

We've included a list of reputable online pharmacies on our website. For the most current list visit our page at https://www.internalmedicineforpetparents.com/pharmacies.html

Pharmacies

Pharmacy 1 information	**Pharmacy 1**: _____ Phone #: _____ Website: _____ Comments: _____ _____ _____ _____
Pharmacy 2 information	**Pharmacy 2**: _____ Phone #: _____ Website: _____ Comments: _____ _____ _____ _____
Pharmacy 3 information	**Pharmacy 3**: _____ Phone #: _____ Website: _____ Comments: _____ _____ _____ _____
Comments	_____ _____ _____ _____ _____ _____ _____

Quality of Life

Quality of Life Scale

A good quality of life is sometimes the hardest thing to be sure of as a pet parent. We all want our pets to live happy, healthy lives, but since our pets do not speak the same language, we do we can't ask them. We can, however, learn to read body language and use some subjective and objective tools to give us a better answer to understanding a pet's quality of life.

Major things to consider include:

- Pain control: is your pet painful?
- Respiratory distress: is your pet having trouble breathing, coughing frequently, wheezing, or other respiratory problem?
- Eating and Drinking: is your pet still eating and drinking, a 'normal' amount?
- Mobile: are they able to get up on their own; is it difficult to do?
- Hygiene: are they able to keep themselves clean?
- Attitude: do they still enjoy their favorite things; are they irritable; do they remember you?
- Family: can the family still provide the level of care needed for the pet's condition?

It can be hard to be objective, so we created this Quality of Life Scale that can be used in this journal as your pet's QOL#. You can record the QOL# on a daily, weekly, and monthly basis. You can also mark notes in your monthly tracker which scale was an issue. For example, if your pet's appetite was decreased you may enter E=3 so you can see at a glance if there was an issue. Also, you can add all the numbers up for a week, divide by 7, and get your weekly average score.

If you are looking for more information about quality of life, we recommend checking out "Quality of Life Scale" by Dr. Alice Villalobos, and "J-O-U-R-N-E-Y-S: A Quality of Life Scale for Pets" by Dr. Katie Hilst, DVM from journeyspet.com.

	1 point	5 points	10 points
P - Pain Control:	Your pet seems painful, whining, crying, shifting around trying to get comfortable or laying in one spot, despite taking pain medication.	Your pet's pain is controlled most of the time with pain medication.	Your pet does not have pain.
R - Respiratory Distress:	Your pet is having episodes of extremely labored breathing including: open mouth breathing/gasping, coughing, or difficulty breathing. They may not want to drink or eat because it is difficult to breath. Seek IMMEDIATE veterinary attention.	Your pet experiences episodes of coughing, wheezing, or some exercise intolerance. These last a short amount of time (less than 2-4 minutes) and your veterinarian has prescribed medication to help shorten these issues.	Your pet does not experience any respiratory issues.
E - Eating and Drinking:	Your pet refuses to eat food or drink water. They may be vomiting, diarrhea, or both. They may be nauseous (drooling, lip smacking, or turning their head away after smelling food).	Your pet is eating less than they used to, and don't seem as interested. They make take several trips to the bowl to finish a meal. They may have a decrease or increase in their water intake.	Your pet is eating and drinking normally.

21

	1 point	5 points	10 points
H - Hygiene:	Your pet will lay in their own urine and/or feces. They may have urinary or fecal incontinence (unable to control going to the bathroom) They may have a tumor or mass that requires bandages or cleaning, is infected or bleeding. Your pet may have pressure sores from not getting up.	Your pet may require assistance to urinate and/or defecate but they still try to not lay in it. They are able to hold their feces or urine until they get to an appropriate area. They may have an external tumor or mas but it is not infected or bleeding and may or may not be covered. They are still grooming themselves, but may get everything.	Your pet can urinate, defecate, and groom themselves normally. They do not have any medical issues that cause bad odors.
A - Attitude:	Your pet does not want to spend time with their family. They may hide. They may bite, get irritable, or annoyed if bothered. They may not want to be petted or don't care if they are being pet. Can they remember where they are? Do they not spend time in their favorite spots?	Your pet is spending most of their time with family, but does hide more. They are still happy to greet you when you come home.	Your pet enjoys being part of the family and still participates in normal activities.

	1 point	5 points	10 points
M - Mobility:	Your pet can not walk or stand without assistance.	Your pet can move around on their own with pain medication. They still participate in some normal activities but they may not be able to do them for as long as they used to.	Your pet is fully active and participating in their favorite activities.
F - Family:	You are constantly worried about your pet's health. You do not understand what is happening to them, or how to help. You may feel you are unable to provide for them emotionally, physically, or financially. You may feel exhausted from continuous care. Your pet's health may be the subject of disagreements in the family.	You understand your pet's condition and feel fairly comfortable with the level of care needed. You may have concerns, but they are not overwhelming.	You are able to meet all of your pets needs and do not have any concerns.

P	R	E	M	H	A	F	TOTAL QOL#

Treatment Journal

Month: _____

Month 1: _____

Comment	Sunday	Monday	Tuesday
Week's QOL#	QOL#	QOL#	QOL#
Week's QOL#	QOL#	QOL#	QOL#
Week's QOL#	QOL#	QOL#	QOL#
Week's QOL#	QOL#	QOL#	QOL#
Week's QOL#	QOL#	QOL#	QOL#

General Notes for the Month:

26

Year: 20_____

Wednesday	Thursday	Friday	Saturday
QOL#	QOL#	QOL#	QOL#
QOL#	QOL#	QOL#	QOL#
QOL#	QOL#	QOL#	QOL#
QOL#	QOL#	QOL#	QOL#
QOL#	QOL#	QOL#	QOL#

General Notes for the Month:

Week 1 Dates: _____

Things to Monitor	Sunday	Monday	Tuesday
Appetite			
Water Intake			
Vomit/Regurge/Hairball			
Urination/Defecation			
Coughing/Sneezing			
Energy Level			

Medications

Times			
1			
2			
3			
4			
5			
6			
7			
8			
9			
10			

Week's QOL#	QOL#	QOL#	QOL#

🐾Comments: 🐾

28

Wednesday	Thursday	Friday	Saturday

QOL#	QOL#	QOL#	QOL#

🐾 Comments: 🐾

Week 2 Dates: _____

Things to Monitor	Sunday	Monday	Tuesday
Appetite			
Water Intake			
Vomit/Regurge/Hairball			
Urination/Defecation			
Coughing/Sneezing			
Energy Level			

Medications	Times												
	1												
	2												
	3												
	4												
	5												
	6												
	7												
	8												
	9												
	10												

Week's QOL#	QOL#	QOL#	QOL#

🐾Comments:🐾

Wednesday	Thursday	Friday	Saturday

QOL#	QOL#	QOL#	QOL#

🐾 Comments: 🐾

Week 3 Dates: _____

Things to Monitor	Sunday	Monday	Tuesday
Appetite			
Water Intake			
Vomit/Regurge/Hairball			
Urination/Defecation			
Coughing/Sneezing			
Energy Level			

Medications

Times								
1								
2								
3								
4								
5								
6								
7								
8								
9								
10								

Week's QOL#	QOL#	QOL#	QOL#

Comments:

Wednesday	Thursday	Friday	Saturday

QOL#	QOL#	QOL#	QOL#

🐾 Comments: 🐾

33

Week 4 Dates: _____

Things to Monitor	Sunday	Monday	Tuesday
Appetite			
Water Intake			
Vomit/Regurge/Hairball			
Urination/Defecation			
Coughing/Sneezing			
Energy Level			

Medications

Times			
1			
2			
3			
4			
5			
6			
7			
8			
9			
10			

Week's QOL#	QOL#	QOL#	QOL#

🐾Comments: 🐾

Wednesday	Thursday	Friday	Saturday

QOL#	QOL#	QOL#	QOL#

🐾 Comments: 🐾

Week 5 Dates: _____

Things to Monitor	Sunday	Monday	Tuesday
Appetite			
Water Intake			
Vomit/Regurge/Hairball			
Urination/Defecation			
Coughing/Sneezing			
Energy Level			

Medications

Times													
1													
2													
3													
4													
5													
6													
7													
8													
9													
10													

Week's QOL#	QOL#	QOL#	QOL#

Comments:

Wednesday	Thursday	Friday	Saturday

QOL#	QOL#	QOL#	QOL#

🐾 Comments: 🐾

Treatment Journal

Month: _____

Month 2: _____

Comment	Sunday	Monday	Tuesday
Week's QOL#	QOL#	QOL#	QOL#
Week's QOL#	QOL#	QOL#	QOL#
Week's QOL#	QOL#	QOL#	QOL#
Week's QOL#	QOL#	QOL#	QOL#
Week's QOL#	QOL#	QOL#	QOL#

General Notes for the Month:

Year: 20_____

Wednesday	Thursday	Friday	Saturday
QOL#	QOL#	QOL#	QOL#
QOL#	QOL#	QOL#	QOL#
QOL#	QOL#	QOL#	QOL#
QOL#	QOL#	QOL#	QOL#
QOL#	QOL#	QOL#	QOL#

General Notes for the Month:

Week 1 Dates: _____

Things to Monitor	Sunday	Monday	Tuesday
Appetite			
Water Intake			
Vomit/Regurge/Hairball			
Urination/Defecation			
Coughing/Sneezing			
Energy Level			

Medications

Times									
1									
2									
3									
4									
5									
6									
7									
8									
9									
10									

Week's QOL#	QOL#	QOL#	QOL#

Comments:

Wednesday	Thursday	Friday	Saturday

QOL#	QOL#	QOL#	QOL#

🐾 Comments: 🐾

Week 2 Dates: _____

Things to Monitor	Sunday	Monday	Tuesday
Appetite			
Water Intake			
Vomit/Regurge/Hairball			
Urination/Defecation			
Coughing/Sneezing			
Energy Level			

Medications

Times			
1			
2			
3			
4			
5			
6			
7			
8			
9			
10			

Week's QOL#	QOL#	QOL#	QOL#

🐾Comments: 🐾

44

Wednesday	Thursday	Friday	Saturday

QOL#	QOL#	QOL#	QOL#

🐾 Comments: 🐾

Week 3 Dates: _____

Things to Monitor	Sunday	Monday	Tuesday
Appetite			
Water Intake			
Vomit/Regurge/Hairball			
Urination/Defecation			
Coughing/Sneezing			
Energy Level			

Medications

Times												
1												
2												
3												
4												
5												
6												
7												
8												
9												
10												

Week's QOL#	QOL#	QOL#	QOL#

🐾Comments:🐾

Wednesday	Thursday	Friday	Saturday

QOL#	QOL#	QOL#	QOL#

🐾 Comments: 🐾

Things to Monitor	Sunday	Monday	Tuesday
Appetite			
Water Intake			
Vomit/Regurge/Hairball			
Urination/Defecation			
Coughing/Sneezing			
Energy Level			

Medications

Times			
1			
2			
3			
4			
5			
6			
7			
8			
9			
10			

Week's QOL#	QOL#	QOL#	QOL#

🐾Comments: 🐾

Wednesday	Thursday	Friday	Saturday

QOL#	QOL#	QOL#	QOL#

🐾 Comments: 🐾

Week 5 Dates: _____

Things to Monitor	Sunday	Monday	Tuesday
Appetite			
Water Intake			
Vomit/Regurge/Hairball			
Urination/Defecation			
Coughing/Sneezing			
Energy Level			

Medications

Times														
1														
2														
3														
4														
5														
6														
7														
8														
9														
10														

Week's QOL#	QOL#	QOL#	QOL#

🐾Comments:🐾

Wednesday	Thursday	Friday	Saturday

QOL#	QOL#	QOL#	QOL#

🐾 Comments: 🐾

Treatment Journal

Month: _____

Month 3: _____

Comment		Sunday	Monday	Tuesday
Week's QOL#		QOL#	QOL#	QOL#
Week's QOL#		QOL#	QOL#	QOL#
Week's QOL#		QOL#	QOL#	QOL#
Week's QOL#		QOL#	QOL#	QOL#
Week's QOL#		QOL#	QOL#	QOL#

General Notes for the Month:

Year: 20_____

Wednesday	Thursday	Friday	Saturday
QOL#	QOL#	QOL#	QOL#
QOL#	QOL#	QOL#	QOL#
QOL#	QOL#	QOL#	QOL#
QOL#	QOL#	QOL#	QOL#
QOL#	QOL#	QOL#	QOL#

General Notes for the Month:

55

Week 1 Dates: _____

Things to Monitor	Sunday	Monday	Tuesday
Appetite			
Water Intake			
Vomit/Regurge/Hairball			
Urination/Defecation			
Coughing/Sneezing			
Energy Level			

Medications

Times												
1												
2												
3												
4												
5												
6												
7												
8												
9												
10												

Week's QOL#	QOL#	QOL#	QOL#

🐾Comments: 🐾

Wednesday	Thursday	Friday	Saturday

QOL#	QOL#	QOL#	QOL#

🐾 Comments: 🐾

Week 2 Dates: _____

Things to Monitor	Sunday	Monday	Tuesday
Appetite			
Water Intake			
Vomit/Regurge/Hairball			
Urination/Defecation			
Coughing/Sneezing			
Energy Level			

Medications

Times															
1															
2															
3															
4															
5															
6															
7															
8															
9															
10															

Week's QOL#	QOL#	QOL#	QOL#

🐾Comments: 🐾

Wednesday	Thursday	Friday	Saturday

QOL#	QOL#	QOL#	QOL#

🐾 Comments: 🐾

Week 3 Dates: _____

Things to Monitor	Sunday	Monday	Tuesday
Appetite			
Water Intake			
Vomit/Regurge/Hairball			
Urination/Defecation			
Coughing/Sneezing			
Energy Level			

Medications

Times			
1			
2			
3			
4			
5			
6			
7			
8			
9			
10			

Week's QOL#	QOL#	QOL#	QOL#

Comments:

60

Wednesday	Thursday	Friday	Saturday

QOL#	QOL#	QOL#	QOL#

🐾 Comments: 🐾

61

Things to Monitor	Sunday	Monday	Tuesday
Appetite			
Water Intake			
Vomit/Regurge/Hairball			
Urination/Defecation			
Coughing/Sneezing			
Energy Level			

Medications	Times													
	1													
	2													
	3													
	4													
	5													
	6													
	7													
	8													
	9													
	10													

Week's QOL#	QOL#	QOL#	QOL#

🐾Comments: 🐾

62

Wednesday	Thursday	Friday	Saturday

QOL#	QOL#	QOL#	QOL#

🐾 Comments: 🐾

Week 5 Dates: _____

Things to Monitor	Sunday	Monday	Tuesday
Appetite			
Water Intake			
Vomit/Regurge/Hairball			
Urination/Defecation			
Coughing/Sneezing			
Energy Level			

Medications	Times													
	1													
	2													
	3													
	4													
	5													
	6													
	7													
	8													
	9													
	10													

Week's QOL#	QOL#	QOL#	QOL#

Comments:

64

Wednesday	Thursday	Friday	Saturday

QOL#	QOL#	QOL#	QOL#

🐾 Comments: 🐾

65

Treatment Journal

Month: _____

Month 4: _____

Comment	Sunday	Monday	Tuesday
Week's QOL#	QOL#	QOL#	QOL#
Week's QOL#	QOL#	QOL#	QOL#
Week's QOL#	QOL#	QOL#	QOL#
Week's QOL#	QOL#	QOL#	QOL#
Week's QOL#	QOL#	QOL#	QOL#

General Notes for the Month:

Year: 20_____

Wednesday	Thursday	Friday	Saturday
QOL#	QOL#	QOL#	QOL#
QOL#	QOL#	QOL#	QOL#
QOL#	QOL#	QOL#	QOL#
QOL#	QOL#	QOL#	QOL#
QOL#	QOL#	QOL#	QOL#

General Notes for the Month:

Week 1 Dates: _____

Things to Monitor	Sunday	Monday	Tuesday
Appetite			
Water Intake			
Vomit/Regurge/Hairball			
Urination/Defecation			
Coughing/Sneezing			
Energy Level			

Medications

Times			
1			
2			
3			
4			
5			
6			
7			
8			
9			
10			

Week's QOL#	QOL#	QOL#	QOL#

Comments:

70

Wednesday	Thursday	Friday	Saturday

QOL#	QOL#	QOL#	QOL#

🐾 Comments: 🐾

Things to Monitor	Sunday	Monday	Tuesday
Appetite			
Water Intake			
Vomit/Regurge/Hairball			
Urination/Defecation			
Coughing/Sneezing			
Energy Level			

Medications

Times												
1												
2												
3												
4												
5												
6												
7												
8												
9												
10												

Week's QOL#	QOL#	QOL#	QOL#

🐾Comments: 🐾

Wednesday	Thursday	Friday	Saturday

QOL#	QOL#	QOL#	QOL#

🐾 Comments: 🐾

73

Week 3 Dates: _____

Things to Monitor	Sunday	Monday	Tuesday
Appetite			
Water Intake			
Vomit/Regurge/Hairball			
Urination/Defecation			
Coughing/Sneezing			
Energy Level			

Medications

Times			
1			
2			
3			
4			
5			
6			
7			
8			
9			
10			
Week's QOL#	QOL#	QOL#	QOL#

🐾Comments:🐾

74

Wednesday	Thursday	Friday	Saturday

QOL#	QOL#	QOL#	QOL#

🐾 Comments: 🐾

Week 4 Dates: _____

Things to Monitor	Sunday	Monday	Tuesday
Appetite			
Water Intake			
Vomit/Regurge/Hairball			
Urination/Defecation			
Coughing/Sneezing			
Energy Level			

Medications

Times									
1									
2									
3									
4									
5									
6									
7									
8									
9									
10									

Week's QOL#	QOL#	QOL#	QOL#

🐾Comments: 🐾

Wednesday	Thursday	Friday	Saturday

QOL#	QOL#	QOL#	QOL#

🐾 Comments: 🐾

Things to Monitor	Sunday	Monday	Tuesday
Appetite			
Water Intake			
Vomit/Regurge/Hairball			
Urination/Defecation			
Coughing/Sneezing			
Energy Level			

Medications

Times									
1									
2									
3									
4									
5									
6									
7									
8									
9									
10									

Week's QOL#	QOL#	QOL#	QOL#

Comments:

Wednesday	Thursday	Friday	Saturday

QOL#	QOL#	QOL#	QOL#

🐾 Comments: 🐾

Treatment Journal

Month: _____

Month 5: _____

Comment	Sunday	Monday	Tuesday
Week's QOL#	QOL#	QOL#	QOL#
Week's QOL#	QOL#	QOL#	QOL#
Week's QOL#	QOL#	QOL#	QOL#
Week's QOL#	QOL#	QOL#	QOL#
Week's QOL#	QOL#	QOL#	QOL#

General Notes for the Month:

Year: 20_____

Wednesday	Thursday	Friday	Saturday
QOL#	QOL#	QOL#	QOL#
QOL#	QOL#	QOL#	QOL#
QOL#	QOL#	QOL#	QOL#
QOL#	QOL#	QOL#	QOL#
QOL#	QOL#	QOL#	QOL#

General Notes for the Month:

83

Week 1 Dates: _____

Things to Monitor	Sunday	Monday	Tuesday
Appetite			
Water Intake			
Vomit/Regurge/Hairball			
Urination/Defecation			
Coughing/Sneezing			
Energy Level			

Medications

Times												
1												
2												
3												
4												
5												
6												
7												
8												
9												
10												

Week's QOL#	QOL#	QOL#	QOL#

🐾Comments: 🐾

Wednesday	Thursday	Friday	Saturday

QOL#	QOL#	QOL#	QOL#

🐾 Comments: 🐾

Things to Monitor	Sunday	Monday	Tuesday
Appetite			
Water Intake			
Vomit/Regurge/Hairball			
Urination/Defecation			
Coughing/Sneezing			
Energy Level			

Medications	Times			
	1			
	2			
	3			
	4			
	5			
	6			
	7			
	8			
	9			
	10			

Week's QOL#	QOL#	QOL#	QOL#

Comments:

86

Wednesday	Thursday	Friday	Saturday

QOL#	QOL#	QOL#	QOL#

🐾 Comments: 🐾

Week 3 Dates: _____

Things to Monitor	Sunday	Monday	Tuesday
Appetite			
Water Intake			
Vomit/Regurge/Hairball			
Urination/Defecation			
Coughing/Sneezing			
Energy Level			

Medications

Times			
1			
2			
3			
4			
5			
6			
7			
8			
9			
10			

Week's QOL#	QOL#	QOL#	QOL#

🐾Comments: 🐾

88

Wednesday	Thursday	Friday	Saturday

QOL#	QOL#	QOL#	QOL#

🐾 Comments: 🐾

Things to Monitor	Sunday	Monday	Tuesday
Appetite			
Water Intake			
Vomit/Regurge/Hairball			
Urination/Defecation			
Coughing/Sneezing			
Energy Level			

Medications

Times			
1			
2			
3			
4			
5			
6			
7			
8			
9			
10			

Week's QOL#	QOL#	QOL#	QOL#

🐾Comments: 🐾

Wednesday	Thursday	Friday	Saturday

QOL#	QOL#	QOL#	QOL#

🐾 Comments: 🐾

Things to Monitor	Sunday	Monday	Tuesday
Appetite			
Water Intake			
Vomit/Regurge/Hairball			
Urination/Defecation			
Coughing/Sneezing			
Energy Level			

Medications

Times									
1									
2									
3									
4									
5									
6									
7									
8									
9									
10									

Week's QOL#	QOL#	QOL#	QOL#

🐾Comments: 🐾

Wednesday	Thursday	Friday	Saturday

QOL#	QOL#	QOL#	QOL#

🐾 Comments: 🐾

93

Treatment Journal

Month: _____

Month 6: _____

Comment	Sunday	Monday	Tuesday
Week's QOL#	QOL#	QOL#	QOL#
Week's QOL#	QOL#	QOL#	QOL#
Week's QOL#	QOL#	QOL#	QOL#
Week's QOL#	QOL#	QOL#	QOL#
Week's QOL#	QOL#	QOL#	QOL#

General Notes for the Month:

Year: 20_____

Wednesday	Thursday	Friday	Saturday
QOL#	QOL#	QOL#	QOL#
QOL#	QOL#	QOL#	QOL#
QOL#	QOL#	QOL#	QOL#
QOL#	QOL#	QOL#	QOL#
QOL#	QOL#	QOL#	QOL#

General Notes for the Month:

Week 1 Dates: _____

Things to Monitor	Sunday	Monday	Tuesday
Appetite			
Water Intake			
Vomit/Regurge/Hairball			
Urination/Defecation			
Coughing/Sneezing			
Energy Level			

Medications

Times			
1			
2			
3			
4			
5			
6			
7			
8			
9			
10			

Week's QOL#	QOL#	QOL#	QOL#

Comments:

98

Wednesday	Thursday	Friday	Saturday

QOL#	QOL#	QOL#	QOL#

🐾 Comments: 🐾

Week 2 Dates: _____

Things to Monitor	Sunday	Monday	Tuesday
Appetite			
Water Intake			
Vomit/Regurge/Hairball			
Urination/Defecation			
Coughing/Sneezing			
Energy Level			

Medications

Times												
1												
2												
3												
4												
5												
6												
7												
8												
9												
10												

Week's QOL#	QOL#	QOL#	QOL#

🐾Comments: 🐾

Wednesday	Thursday	Friday	Saturday

QOL#	QOL#	QOL#	QOL#

🐾 Comments: 🐾

Week 3 Dates: _____

Things to Monitor	Sunday	Monday	Tuesday
Appetite			
Water Intake			
Vomit/Regurge/Hairball			
Urination/Defecation			
Coughing/Sneezing			
Energy Level			

Medications

Times											
1											
2											
3											
4											
5											
6											
7											
8											
9											
10											

Week's QOL#	QOL#	QOL#	QOL#

🐾Comments: 🐾

102

Wednesday	Thursday	Friday	Saturday

QOL#	QOL#	QOL#	QOL#

🐾 Comments: 🐾

103

Things to Monitor	Sunday	Monday	Tuesday
Appetite			
Water Intake			
Vomit/Regurge/Hairball			
Urination/Defecation			
Coughing/Sneezing			
Energy Level			

Medications	Times																
	1																
	2																
	3																
	4																
	5																
	6																
	7																
	8																
	9																
	10																

Week's QOL#	QOL#	QOL#	QOL#

🐾Comments: 🐾

Wednesday	Thursday	Friday	Saturday

QOL#	QOL#	QOL#	QOL#

🐾 Comments: 🐾

Things to Monitor	Sunday	Monday	Tuesday
Appetite			
Water Intake			
Vomit/Regurge/Hairball			
Urination/Defecation			
Coughing/Sneezing			
Energy Level			

Medications

Times									
1									
2									
3									
4									
5									
6									
7									
8									
9									
10									

Week's QOL#	QOL#	QOL#	QOL#

🐾Comments: 🐾

Wednesday	Thursday	Friday	Saturday

QOL#	QOL#	QOL#	QOL#

Comments:

107

AFTERWORD

We hope this journal helps you and your veterinary team work together to keep your pet as happy and healthy as possible. Our goal is to make it just a little easier for you, we hope it has.

If this journal helps you and you think others would enjoy it too, we'd love for you to leave a review so other pet owners can find it.

ABOUT THE AUTHORS

Yvonne Brandenburg, RVT, VTS (SAIM) is the founder of Internal Medicine For Pet Parents. She is a Registered Veterinary Technician (RVT) in the state of California and has worked in veterinary clinics since 2003. After working in general practice for seven years, Yvonne challenged herself and became a veterinary technology program instructor. After teaching for several years, being a program director for a year, she then found her way into a specialty hospital. Yvonne obtained her Veterinary Technician Specialist (VTS) designation in Small Animal Internal Medicine (SAIM) in 2016. Since then she has presented at both national and international veterinary conferences, and continues to learn every day.

Ashley DiPrete, RVT, VTS (SAIM) is the co-founder of Internal Medicine For Pet Parents. She attended the Veterinary Technology program at The College of Southern Nevada and received her RVT license in 2009. In 2016 Ashley earned her VTS (SAIM) certification. She is the President of the Academy of Internal Medicine for Veterinary Technicians for the 2019 term. Ashley teaches about internal medicine both online and in person at veterinary conferences.

Internal Medicine For Pet Parents was started in 2018 when Yvonne decided there was a need for pet parents to find reliable information to keep furry family members healthy after being diagnosed with acute and/or chronic internal medicine diseases.

Yvonne quickly realized she needed a partner and Ashley was a perfect fit. They've been working together ever since to share with families as much as they can about the diseases they fight against every day. The goal of the series and the website is to have a place to find veterinary approved information, great resources about the internal medicine diseases pets are diagnosed with, and a place for pet parents to feel connected.

CONNECT WITH US

Sign up to join our newsletter and get a free gift!
http://subscribe.internalmedicineforpetparents.com/journal

For more information, please check out:
https://www.InternalMedicineForPetParents.com

ERNAL MEDICINE FOR PET PARENTS SERIES

are creating references for internal medicine diseases that affect our family members. complete list of the books published in our series, and upcoming releases, please visit website for the most up to date list. Visit: ://www.internalmedicineforpetparents.com/books

Made in the USA
San Bernardino, CA
30 January 2019